C H O O S E !

CH O OS E!

The Role That CHOICE Plays
In Shaping Women's Lives

DOTTIE GANDY & MARSHA CLARK

BROWN BOOKS PUBLISHING GROUP
DALLAS, TEXAS

For information, please contact:
Brown Books Publishing Group
16200 North Dallas Parkway, Suite 170
Dallas, Texas 75248
www.brownbooks.com
972-381-0009

ISBN 0-9744597-9-8

LCCN ??

2 3 4 5 6 7 8 9 10

! DEDICATION

This book is dedicated to all women who have learned, or are learning, to use choice as the powerful tool for which it was intended: giving them the lives they desire and deserve. (That means this book is written for you.)

TABLE !F CONTENTS

ACKN!WLEDGMENTS

FROM DOTTIE GANDY

First and foremost, to my mother Cathryn Bruce, who always has been and always will be my model for a strong, competent, compassionate woman.

To my husband, Tom, who never slows down when it comes to supporting my passions.

To my daughters, Kelly Newman and Rebecca Lopinto, who constantly remind me that I got lucky when they chose me to be their mother.

To those four extraordinary children who call me Grandottie: Mike and Christina Lopinto and Alex and Collin Newman.

FROM MARSHA CLARK

To my husband, Dale, who provides me with unwavering support and love in all I do.

To my sons, Brent and Cory, and my daughter-in-law, Michelle, who make being a mother very, very special and whose love I cherish.

To my grandaughter, Kinsey, who brings a new generation of hopes and dreams to our family.

To my mother, Thelma Manahan, who taught me powerful lessons regarding the role that choice plays in shaping our lives.

To the graduates of the POWER of Self Program, who have blessed my life and who have become dear friends in our journeys together.

FROM BOTH OF US

And a special acknowledgment to the women who willingly and candidly shared their stories with us as we shaped the characters of this book. They provided depth, meaning, and insights into the joys and the challenges that women share. Thank you, Sharon Allman, Mona Bailey, Missy Barlow, Jan Belcher, Linda Cubero, Ellen Debenport, Master Sergeant Lela Derrough, Major Diana Echols, Technical Sergeant Marilyn Edwards, Lt.

Colonel Jay Evans and the staff at the 301st Fighter Wing Family Support Center, Nancy Fares, Mariquita Gordon, Jennifer Granberry, Tracy Henderson, Master Sergeant Robin Johnsen, Amy Newman, Valerie Prater, Tracie Reveal, Kathy Seei, Laura Shepard, Courtnie L. Simpson (daughter of Major Charles H. Simpson), and Master Sergeant Heather Tisdale.

A special thanks to Linda and Louis Brown who provided the perfect writing environment in their lovely bed and breakfast, The Chaska House, in Waxahachie, Texas. The Hemingway Cottage was truly an inspiration.

We want to express our appreciation for the support, insights, and friendship offered by our other colleages in the "Up To Something" group: Brent Snyder, Brint Driggs, LeeAnn Mallory, Fritzi Pikes Woods, Mark Youngblood, and Rand Stagen. It was at a meeting of this group in 2003 that Marsha and I decided to co-author this book.

And to the wonderful team of women at Brown Books Publishing who saw the possibility for this book and made it happen!

FOREW!RD

BY EDIE SEASHORE

DUPED BY SOCIETY— UP UNTIL NOW

How did it all begin? The beliefs we held that we were less than, second-class citizens, voiceless, unable to lead, interruptible, invisible—all because we were women. Where did all that start?

How were we duped by society into believing that for us there were rights and wrongs, limited choices that were acceptable and unacceptable, as society decreed? We went along with being duped, accepting society's choices bestowed on us only because we were women.

It started with our colluding with the beliefs that we had no choices but to buy into society's defining of us. We colluded by accepting the roles, behaviors, and beliefs that rendered us less powerful, less central, and less influential than we deserved to be. We colluded based on the beliefs that we had to in order to be accepted, to fit in, and to fulfill our place in society.

We have gone along—up until now. Now we realize that we can make our own choices—deliberate, intentional, conscious choices. We are changing our beliefs. We are choosing to take control of our actions and our decisions, becoming the persons we would like to be, no longer duped. It is becoming clearer to us that we can reframe our beliefs and greatly expand our choices about the roles we want to fill.

The stories that unfold in this book are vignettes of the vital support we can provide for each other. This support must be deliberate and active, helping us to make and take our own choices. It's not easy to challenge society's socialization. It takes determination, courage, and especially a lot of support from other women also engaged in this challenge. Support that helps us get back on track, continue when we are interrupted, be heard when we lose our voices, and be seen when we are rendered invisible. We can do this for each other—holding these new beliefs.

Making these new choices confuses the "order of the universe," society's scheme of things. Breaking sex-role stereotypes (society's duping) takes commitment. Choose! The Role that Choice Plays in Shaping Women's Lives is a statement of the power of women supporting other women to become more powerful. No longer duped by society, we will be as choosy and as powerful as we believe we can be.

Introduction !

E*verything* that happens to us is the result of a choice we have made or allowed others to make for us.

This book is written to help women clarify what they want in life for themselves and those around them. We encourage them to be more deliberate in their choice-making to achieve their long-term goals and objectives. Specifically, this book is for women who have ever asked themselves the following questions:

1. Where do I find the courage to ask for what I want?
2. How do I reconcile my desire to be a stay-at-home mom with the guilt I feel about missing the stimulation of the workplace?
3. How do I schedule my own needs and desires on my daily agenda?
4. How do I know that I am truly fulfilling my life's purpose when there are so many options?

**5. Why is it that just when life is starting to feel
right, change occurs?**

We believe the answers to these questions are contained
in the day-to-day choices we make.

Both of us have devoted a significant part of our lives to
women and their issues. We wrote this book to provide
another vehicle by which we could inspire and support
women. The book's message is powerful; the format is
simple. When women are at significant choice points in
their lives, they can pick up this book for inspiration.

We continue to be inspired by the thoughtful and
intentional choices made by the women we interviewed
and the many others around us. Women make hundreds
of choices every day. What we choose to wear on any
given day probably won't have a lifelong impact, but the
careers we choose, the messages we send to our children,
and the courage we summon to make personal requests
significantly impact the quality and nature of our lives
and the lives of those around us.

In *Choose!* you will meet five women. The profiles we've
chosen allow every woman to see herself in one or more
of the characters. Although the women are introduced
as characters in a story, interviews were conducted
with real groups of women to explore the critical
choice points in their lives. It is the information from
these women that shapes and forms the characters

you're about to meet. Each of these characters leads a life quite different from the others, but all have a common desire to attend a fictional Intention Convention in Dallas, Texas, where the central theme of the meeting is to examine the role that choice plays in the quality and outcome of women's lives.

In this book, you will meet Rachel (a successful middle manager in a large company), Jennifer (a stay-at-home mom who put her own career on hold to raise her children), Maria (a single mom holding down two jobs as a teacher and a reservist in the Air Force), Grace (a former journalist who became a minister in her middle years), and Kathy (a longtime public servant). We believe you will see parts of yourself as these women explore options and make choices in their unique yet familiar lives.

The first choices these women make relate to the challenges, issues, and questions they face in deciding whether to attend the Intention Convention.

As the lives of these women unfold in the following chapters, they gain the following abilities:

♦ **To see thoughtful choice as their most potent tool in shaping the direction of their lives.**

♦ **To make conscious choices that permanently impact the course, direction, and quality of their lives.**

♦ To understand the distinction between "self" and "selfish" when it comes to making critical choices.

♦ To understand there is never a last choice; there is always a next choice. It's about helping each of us to discover the choices that are right for us at any given point in our lives.

♦ And finally, to be starkly aware that WE ALWAYS HAVE A CHOICE!

We invite you, the readers, and all women to become more intentional and thoughtful about the choices you make at key points in your life. We want those choices to produce lives full of hope and fulfilled expectations. We want you to reconsider those choices that leave you with regrets and disappointments. Because the answer for each of us is so personal, no book will hold the magic answer. We want you to read this book from your own personal perspective. The right conclusion will be exactly the one you draw. We encourage you to read this book for yourself and not to compare yourself to the characters in some judgmental way; rather, draw strength from each of them in ways that speak to you. When we made the decision to co-author a book about women and the role that choice plays in the outcomes of their lives, we were business colleagues. Our "choice" to embark on this writing journey together has taken us to a new level in our relationship. As we shared with each other our own key choice points over the years, we developed a bond that far surpasses that between business colleagues. We became great friends.

Dottie Gandy
Marsha Clark

Women's Intention Convention

This conference is specifically
dedicated and designed for women . . .

- who are learning to ask for what they want
- who are seeking clarity of purpose
- who are gaining confidence in holding their
  boundaries

Are You That Woman?

Chapter !One

RACHEL

Rachel sighs. It has been one of those days at work. *There is clearly more to be done than time to do it in, so, "Why am I entertaining the notion of cleaning out my in-box? The stuff has been there for weeks. Why tackle it now?" The answer is simple. The pressures of the day make tackling the in-box suddenly a preferred chore. Rachel laughs, remembering a recent article she read about women under stress. The article discussed how women display tend-or-befriend behaviors when under stress, instead of the traditional fight-or-flight response. Her snicker is about her "tending" to her in-box. As she sorts the stack of messages, she notices an invitation to a Women's Intention Convention; it catches her eye and her interest.*

In Rachel's nine years with the Glendale Manufacturing Company, she had seen a lot of changes. The company had gone public two years ago and was now faced with quarterly analysts' calls that required stellar performance and a crystal ball for predicting consistent and ever-increasing earnings. For the first time in its seventy-five-year history, the company was struggling to meet its profit targets. When Glendale had gone public it had been necessary to set up regional call centers. Rachel had always been involved in customer service, but now the company was operating in a national rather than regional market. Rachel had started as an assistant to the Quality Control director and had steadily gained recognition in the company for her hard work and dedication. She had found a way to succeed in what was an otherwise male-dominated organization. As the company grew, Rachel's responsibilities grew. She is now responsible for managing one hundred people in three regional call centers. Women make up the majority of her team.

Re-reading the e-mailed invitation, Rachel becomes intrigued about the notion of a conference that teaches choice making from an intentional and thoughtful place. "Now there's a thought. Me doing something for myself! When was the last time I made that choice?"

Rachel's immediate thoughts are doubtful. Would her company allow her to go? What would her boss think about her request to attend a women's program? Although the company had always accommodated Rachel's desire to attend conferences, previous trips had been related to her specific line of work. Because profit margins had been shrinking, Rachel concluded that his would not be the best time to ask the company for a business-paid trip to any meeting, especially a Women's Intention Convention. The invitation couldn't have come at a worse time. "I guess I could just ask for a week of vacation and pay for it myself." But again, there were others to consider. What would her husband think? After all, they had talked about using a week of their vacation time to finally remodel the bathroom. And, of course, there was the matter of childcare. Although her mother-in-law had willingly cared for the children in the past, Rachel wonders how she would view Rachel's choice to do something just for herself.

Once again, Rachel sighs at the familiar feeling that has surfaced. The well-being of everyone else comes first. It's an automatic thought process. It happens so fast, she has to catch herself. When will she choose to do something for her own well-being? "Is the Intention Convention an opportunity to finally do something for me?" She asks herself, "Do I really want to go? Am I looking for an escape? What is this really all about?"

Rachel begins to think about some of the critical choices she had made in her life. Like her decision, after two years of college, to marry her high school sweetheart, Bill. After marrying, she had worked and supported her husband while he finished his degree. She had always intended to go back to school once her husband graduated and god a job. That decision was delayed when she became pregnant with her first child. Although she chose to stay home after her first child was born, Rachel and her husband soon realized that additional income was necessary. Her husband's career was just getting off the ground. When her first child was a year old, Rachel noticed that the Glendale Manufacturing Company was opening its first plant in their community. She applied for a job and was hired right away.

It wasn't long after Rachel started at Glendale that she began to wonder if she was really starting a career of her own rather than just taking a job to supplement their family income. She loved the work she was doing, and her bosses seemed to really appreciate her work and the contributions she made. But now, twelve years and a second child later, there is no question about giving up her job to stay at home. Too many people are depending on her. The company depends on her to run the call centers and keep problems out of their offices. Her husband appreciates the second income and admires her ability to manage her job, her home, and her family. And her children know that she is always available whenever they need her.

Rachel begins to wonder, "Why am I thinking about these critical choices now? Is there a special message in this invitation for me? I enjoy my life, yet most of my choices have been driven by putting others first. What might my future life be like if I take a more active role in the choices that affect my life? What about some of those old dreams that have fallen by the wayside? Could the convention help me rekindle some of those dreams? Remember how I always wanted to finish my degree . . ."

So Rachel prints out the invitation, puts it in her briefcase, and decides to talk with her husband before showing it to her boss. During her drive home, she begins to formulate the conversation she will have with her husband later that night. Will her husband see her request as a selfish one? Once home, however, she follows her typical routine of getting a meal on the table, helping the kids with their homework, and squeezing in some family fun time before the kids go to bed. It was after nine o'clock that night before Rachel has an opportunity to talk with her husband Bill.

"An opportunity came across my desk today that really has me excited, and I want to talk to you about it. I received an invitation to something called the Intention Convention that will be held in Dallas later this year. The purpose of the convention is to help women make more thoughtful and intentional choices. I would really like to go and I haven't decided whether to ask my boss about paying for it. Given the financial struggles of the company, this may not be the best time to ask them to sponsor my attendance. You know, they've been generous in the past where meetings related to training and development opportunities, but this one feels different. So another thought I have is to use a week of my vacation and pay for my own attendance at the convention. I understand this would have consequences for our family since we had talked about using vacation time to remodel the bathroom. We would also need to have someone help out with the children while I'm gone. I really think this is something I want to do for myself, but because it affects our family, I'd like to hear your thoughts."

As Rachel waits for Bill's response, she sees a smile cross his face, yet doesn't know where his thoughts are going.

"I'm smiling because I've wondered when the time would come that you would want to do something for yourself because it was right for you. Rachel, I love you for the many choices you've made to put the kids and me first. I am so proud of what you've accomplished. Our children are healthy and well cared for, you have supported me through school and my career, and you've clearly been successful at Glendale Manufacturing. If the company chooses not to financially support your participation, then I say the bathroom remodel can wait. We've lived with the bathroom this long. I think you should go, and it's up to you whether you use vacation time or pay for it through the company."

"Bill, your support is important to me. And I appreciate the pride you've just expressed about who I am, as a Mom, a wife, and a manager. I will ask my boss tomorrow if he will sponsor me and I can do that with greater confidence because I know I have your support."

Rachel falls asleep that night thinking about what had happened that day. She had paid attention to something that caught her eye, something for her. She had contemplated something for herself and had made a decision to take action. That action had been in the form of a conversation with her husband, during which she had stated clearly what she wanted and what her options were. She had invited his input, and look what happened.

At work the next day, Rachel hands her boss the invitation to the Intention Convention and tells him that she would like to attend have the company sponsor her attendance. From Rachel's perspective, he seems to be thoughtfully considering what he is reading, but then a scowl appears on his face. The inner voice she immediately hears is "Oh my gosh, I screwed up! I should have left well enough alone when Bill said he would pay for me to go. I should have known this male-dominated company would frown on such a request."

Her inner voice is interrupted when her boss says he thinks this is a great opportunity for her, and that his only concern is about the timing. The company's current struggles with profitability would make paying for this convention a hard sell. He asks her if there would be conventions at a later time or if she had other options. Rachel tells her boss that she could take vacation time to attend and could pay her own way. She clarifies with him that the timing of the request is his only concern, and suggests that she could use a week of her vacation instead. Her boss says, "Well, you know, we could give you the week off with pay if you're willing to cover your own expenses for the convention." They agree that this is an acceptable compromise. Rachel asks, "So if I come back next year and ask to attend the second annual convention, the company will pay for my attendance, assuming better financials, right?" Her boss says yes.***

Rachel goes back to her desk and is quite excited about the way things have worked out. She calls her husband to give him the good news, completes the registration form, and places it in her out-box. So her initial "tending" to her in-box results in a completed registration form in her out-box. She is smiling as the phone rings.

*** For those of you who think this was way too easy, wait until you hear Jennifer's story in Chapter 2.

CHAPTER ! TWO

JENNIFER

H*ey, Rachel. It's me, Jennifer. I'm calling because this is one of those days when I'm really missing work. The kids are testing me in every way imaginable, and right now I'm desperate to talk to anyone over the age of ten! I was remembering the days when we had such great talks over lunch at work. Say something that challenges my adult intellect and comes from somewhere other than out of the mouths of babes."*

Jennifer listens with great interest as Rachel excitedly recounts her last twenty-four h ours, and she tries to recall the last time that she felt that excited. Jennifer questions the choice she made to leave the workforce when her twins were born. With a college degree, she had felt like her career was just beginning to take off. Lately, Jennifer seems to be thinking a lot about women like Rachel, who made the choice to return to the workforce even thought she, too, had children at home.

Up until five years ago, when her twins were born, Jennifer had worked with Rachel at Glendale Manufacturing. Though her career had been blossoming, Jennifer had chosen to stay home to care for the children. She remembers the day the twins were born, and that she couldn't imagine leaving her children with anyone else. Of course, both sets of grandparents were had been very supportive of her decision to put her career on hold. And, although her husband had said he would support her choice to go back to work, it was pretty clear that he preferred her to stay home and care for the children. After all, he had become a successful vice president of sales at a large consulting company and could comfortably support his wife and new family. He had seemed relieved when Jennifer made the choice to stay home and embrace her role as a full-time mom. This had seemed a natural choice for Jennifer as she had watched her mother put her teaching career on hold to raise her own family. But in addition to the twins, Jennifer now has an eighteen-month old as well.

Today had been a typical day in many respects. Jennifer had gotten the kids up, taken Judy and Joanie to kindergarten, gone to the grocery store, and the drug store to pick up prescriptions for the kids' never-ending ear infections. She had barely put a dent in her To Do list when it was time to pick the kids up at kindergarten and take them all to Story Hour at the local bookstore. Much to Jennifer's dismay, Judy and Joanie had chosen this day to demonstrate sibling rivalry at its best. Before Story Hour ended, the ear infection medicine was wearing off on the eighteen-month-old. As the noise and activity levels were rising, so was Jennifer's temper. Another day as nurse, chauffeur, homemaker, etc., had caught up with her. Was this really what she had gone to college for?

Jennifer had finally gotten the kids down for an afternoon nap. Knowing that the sitter would be here in half an hour, Jennifer chose to call Rachel before she got dressed to spend the evening at a company dinner with her husband and his sales colleagues. Tonight was her husband John's regional sales meeting, where awards were to be handed out to top-performing salespeople.

Rachel told Jennifer all about the Women's Intention Convention and how she had developed a plan that enabled her to attend. Jennifer asked Rachel, "What does Bill think about you going?" Rachel told her about her conversation with Bill and how she felt supported by his reaction. In the background, Jennifer heard the doorbell ring. The babysitter, Patricia, arrived to take care of the children for the evening. Jennifer returned to the phone and was asking Rachel lots of questions about the convention, and began to get pretty excited about going herself. Rachel and Jennifer's conversation ended with the hope that they might see each other at the Intention Convention.

Jennifer is so excited that she is bubbling to Patricia about the Convention. "I'm really looking forward to talking to John about this on the way home tonight. It's been so long since I've done something just for me." As Jennifer heads upstairs to get ready for the evening, she says out loud to no one in particular, "I'll have to call my old college roommate; maybe Lynn could come along with Rachel and me to the convention. I think I'll call her tomorrow."

As John and Jennifer are driving to the evening's big event, Jennifer tells him excitedly about her conversation with Rachel. She tells John that she, too, has an interest in attending the Intention Convention. John's initial comment is, "You're not going to turn into one of those feminists are you?" Jennifer assures John that this is something that she really wants to do for herself. She tells John that she will get her mother to take care of the kids and the house, and will make sure dinner is prepared each evening she is gone. With a final promise from Jennifer not to burn any bras, John supports her decision to go. They arrive now and exit the car for dinner. Jennifer is excited thinking about the Intention Convention and the chance to have an adult, girl's time out.

As dinner is over and the awards ceremony begins, John is getting a bit anxious. He and Jennifer both know that he has had a very good year from a sales perspective. Little does either of them know just how good John's sales performance had been. John is not only named Regional Sales Manager of the Year, but also National Sales Manager of the Year. The National Sales Award program will be held in San Francisco . . . during the same dates the Women's Intention Convention will be in Dallas. So in spite of her pride in her husband's accomplishments, Jennifer is saddened by the conflicting events. Her sadness is reflected in her silence on the drive home.

John asks, "Is something wrong?" "Not really," Jennifer responds, "it's just that the National Sales Award program is the same weekend as the Intention Convention in Dallas. I can't be in two places at the same time." John responds with, "Oh, I'm sure there'll be another women's meeting next year. It's important for you to be there when I get the award. I'm counting on you to be there." Jennifer snaps, "Well I don't know if there will be another convention next year or not, and I've been to a dozen of these sales meetings with you." Jennifer thinks back on the many times when it was assumed that part of the "contract" to be a stay-at-home mom was also to put her husband's needs above her own. They drove the rest of the way home in silence.

When Jennifer arrives home, the babysitter Patricia rushes to tell her about looking up the Intention

Convention on the Internet and says she thinks it would be something her mom should also attend. With a long face, Jennifer replies, "Well, it looks like I may not be going, after all." Patricia doesn't quite know how to respond and leaves to return home. Jennifer goes upstairs and kisses the children good night. As she and John go to bed, John says he sees no way for Jennifer to attend the convention. Jennifer falls asleep knowing that she loves being a mother and a wife and wondering if that means having to sacrifice her own desires every time.

The next morning, amid the chaos and confusion of most morning, getting the kids ready for kindergarten, feeding the baby, and getting John out the door, John says, "I really wish there was some way for you to go to the convention, but I just don't see how that can happen." Jennifer thinks to herself, "I'm not giving up yet . . . maybe there is a way."

Once Jennifer has taken the twins to school and the baby is down for a morning nap, she decides to get on the Internet and look up the Intention Convention. She compares the dates and schedules for John's meeting with those of the convention and realizes that, by missing only the closing session of the Intention Convention, she can fly to San Francisco in time to see John receive his award. Confident that John will support this plan, she excitedly calls her college roommate Lynn to tell her about the convention and invite her to attend. After all, how many conversations have she and Lynn had about the joys and challenges of being stay-at-home moms and their ongoing, shared desire to create more time just for themselves?

As Jennifer describes the convention and tells Lynn her plan, Lynn's first question is, "Does John approve of your going?" Jennifer says, "Yes. We had a conflict with the schedules, but I think that's been resolved." Lynn is pretty hesitant; she isn't at all confident that her own husband would support such a decision, but she does agree to talk to him about it. Lynn tells Jennifer that she will call her back the following day and let her know if she can attend.

Jennifer immediately calls her mother to make sure that she can keep the kids and take care of things while she's gone. Her mother agrees, but she seems to have some doubt about this convention that Jennifer is so excited about. Her mother questions what could be more important than Jennifer being at John's side when he receives this prestigious award? Jennifer hangs up the phone and sighs. Her mother is one more person Jennifer had chosen to help justify her choices.

As Jennifer had anticipated, when John comes home that night and listens as she explains her plan, he begins to see how everything can work. She assures him that her mother will be there to take care of the kids and that she will be in San Francisco in time for the big awards ceremony. John sees that Jennifer had resolved the issues and supports her plan to attend both events.

As Jennifer goes to sleep this night, she reflects on the events of the last few days. "Who would have thought twenty-four hours ago that I would be scheduling two big events and that everyone would be happy with my choices?" "What I've learned is that you can make choices for yourself without being selfish. You can honor the needs of others and take care of your needs, too."

The spell of Jennifer's good mood is broken when Lynn calls and tells her that she will not be joining her at the convention. When Lynn had asked her husband, he had accused her of violating her agreement to be a full-time mother to their children. He had also said that if she does have to be away from the kids, it shouldn't be at some women's convention. He paid the bills and would not pay for such nonsense. Jennifer listens sadly as Lynn describes her situation. She feels almost guilty that she is able to go and her friend cannot.

Jennifer says to Lynn, "So your choice is to go along with that response?" Lynn quickly responds with, "I have no choice!" Jennifer feels that any further pushing will be futile at this point, and the conversation ends with Lynn expressing her disappointment that they won't be getting together at the convention.

Jennifer is deep in thought. With the extreme response that Lynn got from her husband, Jennifer realizes that we always do have choices. We may not realize it in the moment, but we ALWAYS have a choice. In fact, Jennifer realizes that Lynn has made a choice . . . and who is Jennifer to question that choice? Jennifer recalls something she heard recently about choice." There is no such thing as a bad choice; there is only a next choice." Jennifer chooses to support her friend in the choice she has made. After all, whether their husbands are supportive or not, both women are passionate about their decision to stay at home and raise their kids.

What Jennifer doesn't know is that her decision to attend the Intention Convention has already started to influence the choice of another woman . . . Maria.

Chapter · Three

Maria

Patricia rushes into her house after babysitting Jennifer's children. She hurriedly tells her mother, Maria, about the Intention Convention and hands her the printout. Maria tells her to slow down and give her a minute to read the invitation. Patricia urges her on, almost insisting that her mother attend this convention. Maria can't understand why Patricia is so insistent. Patricia blurts out, "Mom, you have been a single mother most of my life. You've been a loyal schoolteacher, a patriotic soldier, and a terrific Mom. It's about time you rewarded yourself." Then heads off to her room and goes to bed. Maria is emotionally overwhelmed. What a wonderful daughter she has to care so much about her mother. She is reminded of her own passion as a young woman.

Maria was born in a small border town in south Texas. She enlisted in the Air Force immediately following high school graduation. It was her ticket out of a town and a way of life that held little promise for a successful future. The town she grew up in was just too small to offer opportunities for a young woman who wanted to be part of something bigger than herself. She loved her country and wanted to do something to reflect that love. She decided to join the Air Force. Venturing beyond the borders of her small Texas town was as exciting as it was frightening. Within a year of joining the Air Force, Maria found herself stationed in Germany. Not long after her arrival, she met, fell in love with, and married another airman. The next two years turned out to be an emotional roller coaster ride for her. She gave birth to a daughter, Patricia, whom she adored, and found herself divorcing her husband. In addition, it was time for Maria to decide whether to re-enlist or not. Patricia's father wasn't very interested in being a father. Maria knew she would be raising her daughter on her own.

Was the military life the best one in which to raise her young daughter as a single mother? Although enlisting in the Air Force initially had been Maria's ticket out of her small south Texas town, she loved her military career and was proud of the role she played in defending her country. Maria had never really thought of herself as a patriot, but her time in the Air Force had changed all of that. She also loved the structure and security that such a career provided. Faced now with the knowledge that she would be raising her daughter alone, Maria wondered how she could reconcile her love for her job with the challenges its schedule presented.

If she decided to leave the Air Force, Maria knew she could move to El Paso, where her sister lived. Finding a job there would surely be easier than returning to her small hometown. Marie reached what she decided would be the perfect solution. She would move to El Paso, get a job, and join the Air Force Reserves. That way she could also go back to school and get her teaching certificate, enabling her to provide a more stable and secure life for Patricia. By joining the Air Force Reserves, she could also continue to serve her country. After all, Maria's Reserve pay would help finance Patricia's college fund. She left her active-duty status with the Air Force, moved to El Paso, and joined the Reserves. It was an emotional experience for her. She had made some dear friends while on active duty, the kind of friends that you have for life. Would she be able to keep these friends as she moved into the Reserves? Would she make new friends as she entered this new chapter of her life?

Maria got a job in a local bank in El Paso, and enrolled in college. How on earth could she juggle all of these roles? Maria's sister was a big help to her; she kept Patricia in the evenings while Maria went to school. It took Maria six years to finish her college degree and get her teaching certificate. She immediately got a job teaching seventh grade history. She had always loved history and felt like she had contributed to it somewhat by having actively served in Desert Storm. Her personal experiences helped the history lessons come alive for her students. This teaching job enabled her to be at home when Patricia retuned from school. Maria's sister continued to provide support when Maria had weekend and summer Reserve duty. Maria's ability to juggle her roles as a single mother, teacher, and Air Force Reservist, were driven by her desire to provide Patricia with a better life than her own.

Patricia is now sixteen, and seems determined that her mother should consider attending the Intention Convention n Dallas. She knows and appreciates how much her mother has done for her. Everyone loves Maria as one of the best teachers in school. Maria is constantly encouraging Patricia to work hard and tells her that she can be whatever she wants to be with a good education, a strong work ethic, and a good head on her shoulders. Maria always puts Patricia first, and Patricia knows that.

As Patricia heads off to bed, Maria ponders her daughter's comment that Maria should reward herself. What did she mean by that? Maria had spent most of her adult life putting one foot in front of the other, finding a way to deal with things as they occurred. There were always more than enough things to do. She wanted to make certain that she always gave Patricia better choices and options than she had. It had always been a labor of love to do this for her daughter. How long had it been since she considered choices for herself or even stopped to consider whether or not she had choices? Up to this point, she had made unconscious choices that had seemed to be obvious choices at the time, always with Patricia's best interest in mind. She always thought that her time for making personal choices would come after Patricia graduated from college.

So what about this Intention Convention? When was the last time she had left El Paso for anything but Reserve duty? How long had it been since she had taken a vacation? Maria laughs as she realizes that her only vacations came in the form of summer Reserve duty. How much fun was that? Hmmmm . . . four days in Dallas with no one to report to other than herself. For a fleeting moment, she remembers that young girl, fresh from high school graduation, off to see the world. She smiles.

Maria re-reads the material about the convention and realizes that the dates conflict with Patricia's home-coming game and dance. Her immediate thought is, I can't go. Maria goes to bed, dismissing the Intention Convention from her thoughts.

The next morning Patricia is still excited and asks her mother if she read the material. Maria says that she did, but that it conflicted with the homecoming dance, so, of course, she couldn't go. Patricia rolls her eyes, exasperated. "Mom, of course, you can go. There will be other homecoming dances. I can make a videotape for you to see everything. You can help me buy my dress way ahead of time. We can make this work. I want you to do this for you. If you don't go to the convention, I'm not going to homecoming!" Maria can't believe that Patricia is so adamant about her going to the convention. She wonders if she should give this more thought. Maria heads off to school with her daughter's words ringing in her ears, and thinks, "For some reason, Patricia thinks I really ought to consider this. Maybe there is a way I can make this work."

Maria knows there was another person she could consult, who would listen to her with understanding and compassion, Grace. Grace is in New England. Maria uses part of her lunch hour to send Grace an e-mail.

Dear Grace . . .

It's been a while since we last talked. I hope things are going well at church. How large is your congregation now? The last time we talked, it was growing rapidly. I still plan for Patricia and me to come and visit you and to see you lead church services. The image of that seems like such a long way from our time together in Germany.

I have a very important question, and one of the things I've always counted on in our friendship is your support in helping me to find the truth. Last night Patricia shoved a piece of paper in my face which announced that an Intention Convention was to be held in Dallas, Texas. She is insisting that I go. The convention is about helping women clarify what they want in life, encouraging them to make deliberate choices to achieve those goals. The choices for me have always been clear, what's in the best interest for Patricia.

I have to admit that a part of me got very excited about getting away for four days to do something just for me. And then I was immediately consumed by guilt at the thought of doing such a thing for myself. I told Patricia this morning that I would not go. Much to my surprise, Patricia delivered an ultimatum. From my perspective, attending seems like such a selfish act. Patricia says it's about self, not about being selfish.

On the one hand, the decision to go or not go to a meeting in Dallas is not the issue. The real issue is about whether I am willing to do something for myself. It's not about the time or the money, and I can't remember the last time I even thought about what I wanted for me. So help me, Grace, to understand the difference between self and selfish. I'm really confused. Patricia seems to think there's a difference, but I need help sorting it out. I am relying on our friendship and your insights to help me better understand.

Love, Maria

In almost minutes, Maria gets an e-mail response from Grace.

Maria,

I fully agree with Patricia. It has been far too long since you've done something just for you. Maybe Patricia is trying to tell you that just because you do something for yourself that does not automatically make it a selfish act. The best place to sort out self and selfish is at the convention. Of course, you should go!

Love, Grace

Maria finishes the day at school, and Patricia is waiting for her at home. Patricia greets her mother with, "Well . . . ?" Maria shows her the completed registration. Patricia grabs the registration form and says, "If I hurry, I can get this in the mail today. I don't want to give you time to change your mind." Maria just laughs.

Chapter ·Four

GRACE

It was easier for Grace to respond to Maria's e-mail than it was to dismiss from her own mind the thought of an Intention Convention that helped women make more thoughtful choices. As Grace stares at the screen on her PC, she decides to log on to the Women's Intention Convention Web site to find out more about this event that seems so important to Maria and Patricia. She is intrigued by the notion that women would receive support in making the best choices about difficult decisions. Maybe this convention was just what Grace needed to wrestle with the choice she is facing . . .

Grace first met Maria in Germany when Grace was doing a series of articles for her newspaper on women in the military. Grace had been a successful newspaper journalist for ten years. Maria was one of the women Grace interviewed for her article. They hit it off immediately. Grace was struck by the conflicts that Maria was trying to resolve about serving her country by remaining on active duty, while facing the ongoing challenges of being a single parent. Although, as a single woman, Grace had never had to deal with the challenges Maria described, she was struck by the intensity of Maria's passion to find the right answer for both herself and her young daughter. In the years following that interview, Maria and Grace had stayed in touch.   Grace's career soared after she received journalism's highest award for her groundbreaking series of articles on women in the military. Little did Grace know that, within a matter of years, she would face her own series of choices with the same intensity she so admired in Maria.

Grace was at the pinnacle of her journalism career when what started as a still, small voice in her head grew louder and louder. Spiritual faith had always played an important role in Grace's life, and she could no longer ignore the initially preposterous notion that God was calling her to go into the ministry. This "calling" was coming in Grace's middle years, when her journalism career was at its peak! She still remembers all those voices telling her that leaving her very successful journalism career would be a mistake. "What gives you the right? How absurd! You're forty-five years old! Who are you to think you could pull this off, even with God's blessing? Do you really want to leave all this success behind? What if you won't be accepted by churches because you're a woman?" Grace smiles as she remembers her efforts to deal with those voices.

One Sunday while sitting in church, Grace heard her minister say from the pulpit, "If you ignore the still, small voice of God when it's a whisper, it will eventually find you when it's a two by four." The message gave her chills. And Grace found herself staying after the church service that day to talk with her minister. She shared with him what she thought was a calling to be a minister. She also told him about her doubts and what all of her inner voices had been saying. Her minister asked which of her voices was the most refreshing, the one from God or the ones driven by her fears. By the end of the afternoon, Grace had "answered her call" and scheduled a visit to the seminary. She began the application process for ministerial school, and the rest seems like long-ago history.

For the past three years, Grace has been the minister of a small New England church with a devoted congregation of about 250 people. Grace has stopped doubting her calling and found her own spiritual awakening renewed and replenished through her ministerial role. Her congregation loves her and she loves them. And most of the time, this feels like enough, like all she needs, until she receives a letter from her denomination's headquarters asking her to consider accepting a larger role, focused on women in the ministry. This new role would require her to move to her denomination's headquarters and relinquish the congregation that she has grown to love and who has become her family.

Grace feels she had truly been called to the ministry and is now being asked to take on this new role. Is she missing something? Is it another "calling" and she just hasn't recognized it yet? Or is this a test to see if she is true to her original calling to be a minister to this wonderful congregation? Grace prays to God, "Lead me where you need me, and speak to me in ways I cannot possibly misunderstand." The prayer just leaves Grace's lips when she receives Maria's e-mail. Grace immediately kneels in prayer and asks God, "Is this Your answer to my prayer? Am I, too, supposed to go to the convention to find more of Your answers?"

On the following Sunday, Grace finds herself speaking to her congregation from the pulpit about her desire to attend the Intention Convention. She speaks about her own example of seeking God's guidance to show her what direction she should take. They encourage her to attend the Intention Convention and agreed that God might be nudging her there for a reason.

Taking it one step at a time, Grace finds herself in her office, completing the registration form. She finds comfort in knowing that she doesn't have to have all the answers before attending. It is okay to bring her questions with her.

It is not uncommon at all for ministers, especially women ministers, to journal. As Grace sends off her application, she sits down to journal her thoughts.

Journal Entry: Sunday 2003

It's been an amazing few days. This time last week, I was the thoroughly contented minister of a congregation that really has become my family. In some ways it's as if I've married them. And then, the letter arrived asking me to consider taking on the larger responsibility of expanding the role of women in the ministry. As exciting as this opportunity initially sounded, I immediately began to question whether this was a diversion from my spiritual calling or an extension of that calling. So I did what any confused woman of God would do: I knelt in prayer and asked for unmistakably clear guidance. Was the answer to that request in the e-mail I received almost immediately from my friend Maria talking about an Intention Convention in Dallas? That would have almost been too easy.

Maria's e-mail seemed to unleash dozens of questions that have no easy answers. Does God hand out answers at women's conventions? Would leaving this congregation feel like getting a divorce? Is being a minister to this congregation just another step in my life's plan to support women?

So I found myself talking to the congregation from the pulpit on Sunday. Their outpouring of love and support overwhelmed me. And so I have just completed my own registration for the Intention

Convention and sent an email to Maria telling her
I'll be joining her there.

As Grace closes her journal, she smiles, realizing that
she needs to pack for her trip to Boston tomorrow
for the New England Council on Family Violence, yet
another role in which she has found an opportunity to
support women. She is eager to share the events and
thoughts of the last few days with her friend and the
woman who chairs the council, Kathy.

CHAPTER · FIVE

KATHY

Upon her arrival in Boston, Kathy was looking forward to the lunch engagement she had scheduled with Grace to follow the council meeting. Kathy had met Grace two years earlier, when the New England Council on Family Violence had begun. Kathy looked forward to the meetings and recognized their importance in bringing together government agencies, hospitals, churches, businesses, schools, and community leaders to address the tough issue of family violence. She also looked forward to connecting with her new friend, Grace, whom she admired for the brave choice she had made to switch careers and follow god's call. When lunchtime arrived, Kathy and Grace were bubbling over with news, eager to share their recent life events.

Grace opens the conversation by telling Kathy about what has happened to her in the last few days. "Just when I thought I understood my life's calling and my life was settling in, I got a letter asking me to take on more responsibility by helping to enlarge women's roles in the church." Grace then tells Kathy about her plan to attend the Women's Intention Convention in Dallas. It would help her explore her options and find some answers. Kathy laughs out loud as she recognizes the parallel journey her own life seems to be taking.

Kathy shares with Grace her dilemma about whether or not to run for mayor of Quincy, her hometown. Someone on the city council had quietly approached Kathy and asked her to throw her hat in the ring for mayor. Kathy had been the Public Information Officer for the city of Quincy for twelve years, and she had seen the city grow and weather tough economic times. She had handled the job of PIO with tact, skills, and diplomacy, often successfully bringing together adversarial parties. Kathy had been a public servant all her life, a career that suited her passion for community service. She was both flattered and somewhat taken aback by the council member's quiet request that she consider running for mayor. Kathy had always intended her role as PIO to be her last job before retirement. She was in her mid-fifties and her husband would soon be retiring as head of the math department for the local high school. Their children were grown, married, and had blessed them with two wonderful grandchildren. Their lives, indeed, seemed to be winding down in a predictable, comfortable manner.

When she told her husband George about her opportunity to run for mayor, she was surprised at his strong encouragement for her to accept the challenge. George, too, had always had an interest in public service. He had been an active volunteer in many community efforts during their thirty-five years of marriage. George went so far as to tell Kathy he would be her campaign treasurer if she chose to run. All of a sudden, it seemed to Kathy that she needed to take seriously this request to run for public office.

As with Grace, Kathy's head had filled with lots of questions. "Was she willing to put herself through the grueling tasks of campaigning? Could she withstand the inevitable mudslinging?" Although she had been highly successful in her role as PIO, she would be the first woman to run for the elected office of mayor in her town. "Would Quincy support a woman in the role of mayor? Was she woman enough to do it? What impact would it have on her family?" Kathy really enjoyed her role as grandmother and was looking forward to retirement, which would offer her more time to spend with her grandchildren. What would her children think about her decision to run for mayor? And what about those retirement plans she and George had been discussing?

Kathy and Grace are amused by the remarkable and challenging directions their lives seem to be taking them: Two women who are comfortable, successful, and ready to settle in, are now being asked to prove themselves again in a whole new role. Are they up to the challenge? As lunch ends, Grace encourages Kathy to consider attending the Intention Convention. Perhaps it would help Kathy find some answers to her questions as well.

Kathy notes that the convention occurs two weeks before the filing deadline for mayor. Maybe I should go, she thinks. The timing is right and this might be the best way for me to find the answer.

Following the council meeting, Kathy returns home and tells her husband about the conversation she had shared with Grace. She asks him what he thinks about the Intention Convention as a place for her to gain clarity about the next right steps. George suggests that they both go to Dallas, taking a few extra days to clear their heads and strategize about their next steps. George could fly out to join Kathy after the convention, and they would have some private time to talk about their future.

Although Kathy has received positive support from Grace and George, she still has many doubts. She is very unsure about where this journey may take her. What if the clear answer is that she should, in fact, run for mayor? Is that the right choice for her and for her family? Her life seems so settled. Why would she want to take on running for public office? With trepidation and some skepticism, she completes the registration form and finds herself registered to attend the Women's Intention Convention in Dallas, Texas.

Let the ride begin, she thinks.

CHAPTER *SIX

THE RIDE BEGINS

The day to travel to the Women's Intention Convention in Dallas had finally arrived. It's Thursday morning and conference registration starts at noon. Five women, Rachel, Jennifer, Maria, Grace, and Kathy, find themselves sharing a shuttle bus from the Dallas/Fort Worth Airport to the convention hotel. Each one of them is talking about how she made the decision to attend the convention. Their energy levels are high, and amid the chatter, their stories are heard. Each woman can relate to the journey that led to the choices made by the others. It seems like such a short ride to the hotel.

RACHEL'S STORY

Rachel is happy to reconnect with Jennifer, her former colleague at Glendale Manufacturing. They had only talked once since that day when Jennifer had called Rachel to seek adult conversation. Jennifer asks Rachel to reiterate the chain of events that had enabled her to attend the convention. Rachel reminds her that her company had given her paid time off and that she had paid her own expenses for the convention. Since submitting her registration, Rachel had gradually become more comfortable with her decision to do this for herself. Fortunately, her husband and her boss had been almost as excited about her attendance as she had been. Rachel had found herself taking in stride her mother-in-law's raised eyebrows at her attending a women's convention. Raised eyebrows and all, she knew that her children would be well cared for. Her journey had been a pretty easy one. Rachel is now feeling competent, confident, and excited about the next three days. She insists that Jennifer elaborate on her own decision to attend.

JENNIFER'S STORY

On the surface, Jennifer's biggest hurdle had been one of logistics, arranging for her mom to take care of the kids and then getting to San Francisco in time to see her husband receive his award. She is happy that she is on this shuttle bus, but it took some doing to get to the convention. At a deeper level, she wonders how much her husband really supported her decision. He had always made assumptions about his needs coming first. Until now their lifestyle had never challenged those assumptions. Jennifer wonders just how equal this marital partnership really has been.

She is also feeling a bit guilty about her mother's feelings. Jennifer had always tried to please her mother. And after all, this is the first time for her to be away from her children since the baby was born. She is already missing her children and wondering what her mother really thinks about her being away. Is she really fulfilling her roles as a good mother and wife? Reinforcing these feelings of doubt, Jennifer shares Lynn's story about choosing to stay at home with her husband and children because her husband had been adamantly opposed to her going. Should Jennifer have made the same choice? Jennifer renews the promise to herself that she will call Lynn when she returns from Dallas. Jennifer also mentions to Rachel that her babysitter had been very excited about the convention and had planned to encourage her mother to go. Maria taps Jennifer on the shoulder and says, "I think that's me."

MARIA'S STORY

Maria shares with the group that she is at the convention because her daughter had felt strongly about her attending. "I'm not sure I would have done this on my own." As a single mother raising a sixteen-year-old daughter, she had always put her daughter first. Her only time off had been used for her Reserve duty in the Air Force. She planned to use the money she earned as a Reservist to help finance Patricia's college education. Her desire had always been to provide Patricia with more opportunity than she'd had, and she knew that education was a key factor.

Even though Maria had known that she could take the time off from teaching to attend the convention, she had still been unconvinced about coming. It was going to be homecoming week at Patricia's school, and attending the convention meant that she would miss this big event in her daughter's life. But Patricia had remained adamant, insisting that this was something her mother deserved. Maria explains that "It finally was resolved when I sent an e-mail to my friend Grace, seeking her counsel. It was Grace's immediate support that convinced me to come. I have felt great ever since I made the decision. We picked out Patricia's homecoming dress and Patricia promised to make a video of all the events, so here I am. In retrospect, I guess the choice to come wasn't that hard." Grace nudges her and says, "Speak for yourself. Maybe in retrospect it was easy for you, but that wasn't my experience."

GRACE'S STORY

Unlike the rest of you, my battle has not been with bosses, spouses, or children; my battle has been with a spiritual calling. When my life took a 180-degree turn from professional journalism to the ministry, I assumed that was my last major career decision. The calling seemed to be playing itself out in the most comfortable of ways. I then received a letter asking me to take on a larger role in my denomination to expand opportunities for women in the ministry. That letter set my mind reeling. My spiritual calling had settled into an enjoyable routine and I was jolted out of that calm. So my questions were about whether this was a totally new calling, an extension of my original calling to be a minister, or some test of my commitment to the ministry.

Although my congregation wholeheartedly supported my coming to this convention, they don't know that I have received a letter asking me to consider this new role in the denomination. I come to this convention knowing that God will "speak to me in ways I cannot possibly misunderstand." I come with lots of questions, and I hope to leave with a few good answers concerning the choices I am facing. And believe it or not, a conversation I had with my friend Kathy about coming here helped to uncover a similar challenge for her. Kathy, why don't you share your story?

KATHY'S STORY

Kathy was conversing with the woman sitting next to her on the bus. [We'll later expand on the story of this woman who turns out to be the entrepreneur who will later influence a key decision that Jennifer will make upon leaving the convention.] Kathy says she is definitely the wary one among this group of women. She is here with her husband's support but has less confidence and enthusiasm than these women have displayed. Kathy is quiet at first as she reflects on their differences. She is very aware that she is bringing more skepticism to this convention than the others. After all, her long life as a successful public servant really had satisfied her career dreams. She now has a wonderful family with beautiful grandchildren. Life is good. The whole idea of choosing to run for mayor seemed to raise as many questions as it did answers. Kathy shares with the other women that she is so appreciative of the support offered by her husband and the council member who asked her to run, and yet, she has to be sure that it would be the right decision for her. With the filing deadline just a few weeks away, Kathy is hopeful that what she hears at the convention will provide the guidance and answers she seeks.

As the shuttle arrives at the hotel, the women agree to meet for breakfast the following morning to share their insights from the breakout sessions and the keynote presentation they will attend later in the day.

CHAPTER · SEVEN

THE KEYNOTE ADDRESS

*T**he convention hotel ballroom is filled with hundreds of women. The noise level is high as the women enjoy the companionship and camaraderie with each other. Dessert has been served, the lights dim and the keynote speaker is introduced. A hush falls over the crowd as the speaker begins her address.***

"I am honored to have the opportunity to address those of you who, as women, have come here to learn about and embrace the most powerful tool you have at your disposal. That tool is called choice. It is your ally in the best of times and your resource in the most challenging of times. All of us are called upon to make dozens, perhaps hundreds, of choices every day. Some of those have little impact, while others have significant impact, on the direction and quality of our lives. Our purpose at this Intention Convention is to learn how to make intentional and thoughtful choices, even "on the run," such that our lives and the lives of those around us are positively impacted.

"Specifically, I want to accomplish the following in this keynote address:

1. To help you see thoughtful choice as the most potent tool in shaping the direction of your lives.
2. To support you in making conscious choices that permanently impact the course, direction, and quality of your lives.
3. To understand that there is never a last choice; there is always a next choice.
4. To understand the distinction between "self" and "selfish" when it comes to making critical choices.
5. To understand that YOU ALWAYS HAVE A CHOICE!

CHOICE AS OUR MOST POTENT TOOL

"If I asked you to name your most powerful tool when it comes to shaping the direction and quality of your lives, many of you would say education and training, communication skills, or clarity about your life's focus. I want to suggest that your most powerful and potent tool is your ability to make thoughtful choices. While the skill itself is not a difficult one to acquire, the truth is that most of you have never had any training, coaching, education, or even conversation about how to make these kinds of choices.

"Experts have told us for many years that one of the qualities that distinguishes humans from animals is our ability to exercise judgment and free will. While our animal counterparts must be programmed to make certain choices, we have the innate ability to use our free will to make dozens of choices, none of which require programming (although some practice is helpful).

"Regretfully, we make many of our choices based on our moods or how we're feeling in the moment. When we regret some of the things we have said or done, it is usually because we did not choose actions or words that were consistent with our values and beliefs, *even though that option was available to us.* Yelling at our kids because *we* had a bad day usually finds us regretting our tone or temper and eventually apologizing. When something we have worked very hard on at the office is overlooked, we may *feel* like calling in sick the following day or taking some other dysfunctional action. When the car has a flat at the least convenient time, we kick the tire first (although I have yet to see that action inflate the tire!). In other words, many of our choices are "automatic," something we learned from watching others, the television, etc. Many of these automatic responses no longer serve us. Even though we may used these patterns of responding for many years, we have the freedom to change them and to make choices consistent with our values and beliefs. When we do this, choice becomes our most potent and powerful tool.

CHOICES THAT PERMANENTLY IMPACT THE DIRECTION AND QUALITY OF OUR LIVES

"Choosing whether to wear a blue suit or brown slacks to work rarely impacts the quality and direction of our lives. Choosing what to say at an important meeting or how to interact with a challenging child or work colleague can have a permanent impact. Our insistence on constantly berating a child or colleague in the presence of others can influence whether that child grows up with confidence and whether or not that colleague achieves their potential in the workplace. Our relationship with others can be a key determinant when it comes to a promotion at work or a healthy relationship with our friends and family members. Most of us can recall choices we made a long time ago that still affect us today. The choice to forego college, to marry early (or late), to play small rather than utilize all of our capabilities, to berate rather than uplift, all of these represent choice points that permanently affect the outcome of our lives . . .

Up until now!

"While we cannot go back and erase our past bad choices, by utilizing the most potent tool we have, we can make new choices that seem magically to turn our lives around. For example, I chose for many years a lifestyle that was physically unhealthy. I was lazy when it came to exercising and foolish about the foods I ate. I approached middle age with prescriptions for high blood pressure and high cholesterol. I assumed that because my parents lived an unhealthy lifestyle, something in my gene pool kept me from making   choices different from theirs. A friend suggested to me that I could make my own choices, independent of what had happened in the past, and it turned my life around. Although many of my poor diet and exercise choices were difficult to give up, over time I found it increasingly easier to choose a healthier lifestyle. Today I am prescription free, twenty-five pounds lighter, and going to the gym on a regular basis.

"I remember a friend telling me that when she was laid off from her job, she gave her boss a not-so-pleasant piece of her mind and quickly began bad-mouthing her boss and her company to any and all who would listen. Eventually she replaced her bad mood with job search efforts, only to discover that the position she really wanted required her to produce a letter of recommendation from her previous employer. At first, she felt her only choice was to keep looking for another position, even though she really wanted this job. A friend reminded her she had another choice: to clean up the mess she had made of her relationship with her previous boss. Even though talking to him was a daunting task, she nonetheless called him, expressed her regrets about her behavior, and said she understood that a layoff must have been as upsetting for him as it was for her. She said she hoped they could find a way to remain friends, even though they were no longer work colleagues. Her boss told her he appreciated her candor. When she told him about the new position for which she was applying, he asked how he could support her. She said a letter of recommendation would be helpful. He agreed to write the letter and included the fact that, in addition to her other skills, she was an employee who accepted responsibility for her actions, a key asset for any company.

"When Rosa Parks chose to sit at the front of the bus, she changed the course of history forever. Mother Teresa chose a vow of poverty as her way of serving the multitudes, and she changed the lives of millions.

"The choices we make can and do permanently impact the direction of our lives.

THERE IS NEVER A LAST CHOICE; THERE IS, HOWEVER, ALWAYS A NEXT CHOICE

"How many times have we said to ourselves that if we had it do all over, we would make very different choices? As women, we seem especially determined to wear our past mistakes like an albatross around our necks, choking off the possibility of any future other than the one we currently face. We carry our guilt around with us, and simultaneously resent that guilt because we know in our hearts we did the best we could in that moment.

"But we don't have to do is keep making choices that don't serve us or those around us. We can make choices about where we want to go, independent of where we have been. Knowing that we have never made our last choice is refreshing because it then allows us to make choices that move us forward. This requires us to be very clear about where we want to go. Such clarity allows for a wide variety of choices not available to those still stuck in the past.

"Consider the woman who used her time in prison to get a college education so that she could create a new life for herself. Or the mother who received her high school diploma at the same time her daughter did. Or the employee who learned a new language to become more valuable to her company. Or how about the successful corporate executive who pursued her passion for art and found her greatest financial and personal success at the easel and not in the boardroom.

"The key is to focus on what's in front of you, and then make choices consistent with the direction you want to go. The worst choices we made in our past are just that, in our past. There is never a last choice; there is always a next choice.

THE DISTINCTION BETWEEN
SELF AND SELFISH WHEN IT COMES TO
MAKING CHOICES

"This can be a tricky concept to grasp. As women, we have been encouraged to do for others, often putting our needs and ourselves last, and that's assuming we allow ourselves a place on that list at all. Initially, we feel rewarded when we are praised for our helpful support of others in their time of need. Even when we reach the point of exhaustion, we tell ourselves that somehow we must find a way to continue putting the needs of others before our own.

"If always serving others first has become a habit, finding time to honor your own needs quickly becomes labeled as "selfish." Even when we feel depleted physically, mentally, and emotionally, we nonetheless keep on giving. We forget that when we give to the point of depletion, we lose the ability to care for others. Stopping to take care of ourselves, or "sharpening the saw" as some would say, is the only way we can honor a desire to support others. If you are someone who has always put the needs of others ahead of your own, deciding to do something for yourself feels selfish because it is unfamiliar territory.

"The woman who believes that she is at her best when she is working learns to tell her children that she works because they deserve a mother who's at her best. The woman who chooses to stay at home and care for her children must also assure them that her choice is for herself as well as for them. Often, we judge each other for choosing to work outside the home or choosing to be a stay-at-home mom. I say, celebrate that we have those choices! Honor the choices that each of us makes for ourselves, our family, and our loved ones. When women allow others to define what is and isn't a selfish act, a loss of self occurs. This loss of identity has an eroding effect, often diminishing our confidence.

"There is no one right answer that defines the distinction between self and selfish. It is a choice each woman must make for herself. What is selfish for one woman may be an act of self for another. The key is taking responsibility for defining our own labels, rather than allowing others to assign those labels.

"There are those who talk about enlightened self-ishness, the kind of paying attention to one's needs that ultimately benefits everyone. It's about replenishing ourselves so that we have plenty to give to others, which recognizably is so important to women.

"Giving until it hurts is just that, a hurtful experience. Giving as a choice that embraces our own needs as well as those around us is the ultimate act of "self.""

REMEMBER THAT WE ALWAYS
HAVE A CHOICE

"Those of us who go through life as victims of our circumstances do so because we have decided that we have no choice in the matter. This is painfully true in the case of women who stay in abusive relationships because they believe there is no other way out. It is equally true of women who stay in dead-end jobs because they believe they have no other choice. It is true of women who abuse substances because they believe their addiction was the last choice they had.

"Living life as a victim makes us a sour old person. Our only recovery is learning that we always have a choice in any situation. The woman who says she has no choice but to stay in a dead-end job is *choosing* to continue working there. When we say we have no choice but to stay in an unhealthy relationship ("for the sake of my kids, or my lifestyle, or the money"), we are still *choosing* to stay in that relationship! When we say we have no choice but to go through life without an education, we are *choosing* the continuation of that lifestyle.

"While we all know that the payoff for being a victim is the absolution of all responsibility for how our lives turn out, what we forget is that we choose to be a victim. We are perpetuating the very life that we despise. We are colluding in the marginalization that we abhor.

If you leave this convention with having only learned than that you always have a choice, we will have succeeded in our purpose.

"The good news is that we always have a choice.

"Going from this place, what will your choices be?"

The opening keynote now ends. The five women disperse with others to attend breakout sessions to further explore some of the ideas they heard in the speech. In the following chapter, you will see the handouts given at the five breakout sessions that our women attended. Each of the handouts provides a rationale statement, an example, and objectives for learning.

The women have agreed to meet for breakfast the following morning to compare notes and share what they learned at the breakout sessions.

CHAPTER ·EIGHT

THE BREAKOUT SESSIONS

BREAKOUT SESSION #1
CHOICE AS A POWERFUL TOOL

RATIONALE

Data shows us that when women make choices, it is often from a place of default, i.e., it seemed like the thing to do in the moment. While such choices can sometimes be appropriate, more often than not we find ourselves after the fact questioning the rightness of our decision. When we catch ourselves saying, "I wish I had said or done something different," it usually indicates that our choice was hastily rather than intentionally made. Our ability to stop at significant choice points and consider our options makes choice one of our most potent tools.

EXAMPLE

Consider the mother who returned from work one evening to find her four-year-old son proudly displaying a dead fly he had swatted in an effort to be "helpful." He seemed oblivious to the fact that he had also smashed a favorite vase in his effort to swat the fly. He proudly displayed the dead fly, unaware of the temper building inside his mother. Can't he see what he's done! she silently fumed to herself. That vase was inexpensive but it had a lot of sentimental value. How could he be so careless! A good spanking and talking to should teach him better!

Had the mother acted on the instincts her temper was urging, she would have probably overreacted in terms of what she said and the spanking that followed. It was in a split second before she reacted that she remembered she had a choice. Although the vase had sentimental value, the mother knew it could be easily replaced. What could not be changed easily was the emotional damage she might have inflicted had she fully vented the anger she was feeling.

Instead, she chose to kneel down, hug her son, and thank him for killing the fly. (She probably also had a conversation with him later about safer ways to swat a fly.)

The ability to make another choice based on values (she loved her son and wanted him to feel appreciated when he did something he thought was helpful) rather than circumstances, feelings, or emotions (rage, anger, upset) helped this mother foster the kind of relationship she wanted her son to have with his own children some day.

In this breakout session, participants will learn the following:

1. The ability to make intentional, thoughtful choices is one of our most powerful tools when it comes to nurturing and sustaining relationships.
2. In those situations that are driven by emotions or circumstances, our instinctive responses almost always leave us with regrets or misgivings.
3. Learning to make choices aligned with our values, rather than our feelings, significantly impacts the direction and quality of our lives.

BREAKOUT SESSION #2
LEARNING HOW TO MAKE THE RIGHT CHOICE

RATIONALE

The gap between knowledge and action is one that has frustrated us for many lifetimes. Knowledge is insufficient if we are not willing to attach the required and appropriate action. Reading a diet book, for example, will not help us shed pounds. We actually have to do what the book is asking us to do if we want the knowledge to translate into results. Likewise, knowing how to choose a response based on our values implies that we need to identify our values. Few of us have ever engaged in the mental exercise that helps us clarify our values, those values that define who we are and may or may not align with the values imposed by others. The ability to translate what we know and want for ourselves into appropriate and consistent choices is what this session will address.

EXAMPLE

A mother trained for nine months to run her first marathon. Her excitement about the upcoming race diminished when she learned that her daughter's soccer team (which she coached) had made the playoffs for the first time. She then had to choose between her role as a coach and her desire to run the marathon, which was on the same Saturday as the first playoff game. When she realized that her personal mission statement said a lot about her role as a mother, but nothing about being a marathon runner, she knew which choice to make. She coached her daughter's soccer team in their first playoff game. About six weeks later, she had another opportunity to run a marathon, and did so.

This mother's choices were not between right and wrong, but between better and best. Being clear about her values in life helped her make the right decision. Another mother whose key value was one of physical well-being might have chosen to run the first marathon. Knowing what we want for ourselves is the key to making good choices.

In this breakout session, participants will learn the following:

1. Knowing what we value requires thoughtful consideration and time spent clarifying those values.
2. When we find ourselves in situations that require us to choose between two or more equally compelling options, we choose based on our values.
3. Knowing what we value and acting on those values guarantees us a sense of purpose and fulfillment.

BREAKOUT SESSION #3
THERE IS ALWAYS A NEXT CHOICE

RATIONALE

It is easy to get hooked on the notion that we have exhausted all of our available choices and are thereby doomed to live out our lives with the regrets of past bad choices. Many of us believe that because we said or did something that we now regret, we must resign ourselves to a future of doomed relationships, lost careers, and missed opportunities. When we hear ourselves saying, "If only I had it to do over again . . ." it's as if we have foreclosed on any and all options for recovery. Our lives, careers, and relationships become things we have "settled for" and a mood of resignation defines our life. A better idea is the belief that we have never made our last choice, because we always have a next choice. This session helps us see what can happen to our lives when we surrender the notion that we have no more choices.

EXAMPLE

Thirty years into her career, a successful corporate executive had begun to ask herself whether she had the interest and desire to spend another five years plugging away at what she did well, just to qualify for her retirement. She had recently become intrigued with an idea she thought would be good content for a book. When she considered her age and her circumstances, however, "logic" suggested that writing a book was a foolish notion; the time to have written a book would have been many years ago, when she moving up in her career. When she mentioned the notion of writing a book to her family and friends, they also suggested that her time to make that kind of choice had come and gone. They were quick to point out that her life as she knew it was pretty good.

However, something about the finality of her career options didn't make sense. What if she could make another choice? Could she succeed? Would she be tampering with good choices she had already made? In terms of her choices, leaving well enough alone seemed to be the given. But proving that we all, indeed, have a next choice, she gulped and resigned from what had been a terrific job and found herself attending a writer's conference. The rest is history. Her first book was published at the age of sixty-one, and her second book was published at the age of sixty-four.

There is never a last choice; there is always a next choice.

In this breakout session, participants will learn the following:
1. When we say we have no more choices, that's a choice!
2. In relationships, careers, and life pursuits, there is never a final choice; there is always

a next choice that allows us to continually define and redefine who we are.

3. Knowing that there is always a next choice gives us the freedom to stay confidently in the present as we have defined it.

BREAKOUT SESSION #4
UNDERSTANDING THE SELF IN SELFISH

RATIONALE

Many of us accomplish a myriad of tasks each week. Whether or not we took into account our own interests. In other words, when our lives (or weeks) are filled with honoring the agendas of others to the exclusion of our own interests and well-being, we experience exhaustion. When an equally busy week has us honor our own agendas as well as those of others, we feel exhilarated. The most dedicated of women, who relentlessly find themselves in service to others at the expense of their own needs, eventually run out of steam. When this happens, rather than begin the task of self-replenishment, we somehow find one more way to "suck it up" and keep going. The dysfunction of this behavior is as obvious as it is abused. Only when we learn to honor the needs of others in balance with honoring our own do we fully become the women we are designed to be.

EXAMPLE

She grew up with a mother who seemed to have an endless capacity to serve others. In fact, her mother often said she thrived on doing for others. It was not until her mother died of a stroke in her mid-fifties that she began to question her mother's definition of service, which seemed to exclude her own needs. She had always been taught, at home and at church, that service was one of the highest expressions of a good person. At work, she had been praised and promoted for always putting the demands of the company ahead of her own. But service to the exclusion of self seemed too high a price.

When she looked in the mirror one day, she saw her mother rather than herself and knew that she was choosing the same path that had led to her mother's early death. In that moment, she sat down and listed those things that were important to her and which she had permanently parked on the back burner of her life. In college she had been a great athlete, although in the past ten years she had hardly taken the time for an occasional walk. And although she promised her children her work would never come first, she knew that she had missed far too many of their school activities. Even her husband complained that she was rarely available for quality time or even fun.

So she reorganized her life, always placing on her weekly schedule those things that were most important to her. In fact, her early-morning runs seemed to give her more energy for the tasks at work. And leaving early from time to time to attend one of her kid's school events didn't threaten her career as she had always assumed it would. She had finally figured out that honoring her own needs was the real way to serve.

In this breakout session, participants will learn the following:

1. "Self" is in the word selfish for a reason.
2. Only by honoring and including our needs along with those of others can we truly serve.
3. It is in the honoring of self that we become fully expressed as women, and others are served by this recognition.

BREAKOUT SESSION #5
WE ALWAYS HAVE A CHOICE

RATIONALE

Most simply defined, a victim is one who believes she has no choices. She has allowed events, circumstances, and other people to make choices for her. She believes others when they say that without them she has no choice. No single concept has done more damage to the human psyche than the belief that we have no choice. In truth, there is no such thing as any choice. When we stay in a bad situation, at work or at home, because we believe we have no choice, we are really telling ourselves that any other choice might be worse than the one we're making. In other words, we are *choosing* to stay where we are by declaring that we have no other options. When we understand and accept the premise that we always have a choice, life becomes full of possibilities.

EXAMPLE

For twenty-five years she had stayed in a marriage that had soured long ago. She had been raised to believe that once you made the choice to marry someone, that decision became inviolate, and so she had *chosen* to stay in a dysfunctional relationship that no longer served her. She watched others who seemed to know how to make their marriages work and wished that she had another chance to participate in a marriage relationship that sweetened rather than soured as the years went by.

One day one of her children (now grown) asked her why she continued to stay in a relationship that no longer served her. She replied, "I have no choice." Her son replied, "What if you did?" Slowly but surely she began to envision a life for herself outside of a failing marriage. She enrolled in an internet language course and become fluent in a second language, one that guaranteed her employment inside or outside of a marriage. When she finally approached her husband about a divorce, he seemed more relieved than surprised.

Today she is a bilingual educator who has fallen in love with the person she has become (and with one of her fellow teachers). She did, in fact, have a choice.

In this breakout session participants will learn the following:

1. We always have a choice, period.
2. When we honor the belief that we always have a choice, life shows up differently around us.
3. We always have a choice, period.

CHAPTER ·NINE

BREAKFAST

T *he five women join for breakfast as planned. All had attended the keynote address the day before and several breakout sessions in the afternoon. Their moods seem to range from excited to pensive, from anxious to reflective. Rachel opens the conversation with great elation.*

RACHEL'S STORY

"I knew I was anxious to come to this convention, but I'm getting insights and answers that I could never have anticipated. I have so many more choices than I thought I did. I am more convinced than ever to finish my college education. I believe I can even get my company to provide tuition reimbursement. Lots of ideas to improve our Call Centers are floating around in my head. I believe these ideas will contribute to Glendale's profits. Never have I felt more confident about my career. Yes, my career! It's no longer just a job that provides additional family income."

Even as Rachel shares her excitement with the other women, she realizes that she now has a whole new set of choices to make. For one thing, returning to college will have an impact on her family life, and will require her husband Bill to be more actively involved on the home front. She knows he is proud of her, but will he be as enthusiastic about taking on more responsibility with the kids and the house? Her return to college will also mean that she will have to negotiate with her son about how many baseball games she can attend. And her daughter might have to find other means of transportation to her soccer games from time to time. Even with all of these new decisions facing her, Rachel remains enthusiastic and confident that she can find the ways to make it all work.

That's a funny thing about choices: Each one seems to generate several more. I guess it's like the keynote speaker said, "There's never a last choice, only a next choice."

JENNIFER'S STORY

"I'm enthusiastic for some of the same reasons Rachel shared. Part of me came to this convention as a way to escape for a few days the tedium that goes with being a stay-at-home mom. I don't regret for a minute my decision to stay at home with the kids. At the same time, there are lots of days when I miss the excitement and stimulation that my work life provided. Until this convention, the pull and tug between caring for my children and the desire to return to some kind of work existed as an either/or thing for me. But an amazing conversation with one of the other women attendees has helped me to see things differently.

"I was in a breakout session with Kelly, another stay-at-home mom who, like myself, left a successful career to care for her children. But she had wanted to find a way both to care for her kids and return to work. And guess what? She did! Kelly now has a computer -,training business that she operates out of her home. She schedules her business appointments around the hours her kids are in school. When emergencies arise, she has the flexibility to reschedule her appointments. She's been doing this for almost two years and is even starting to make a profit. She loves the flexibility her home-based career provides and even more she loves the time she continues to share with her children. She's fulfilling her commitment to care for her children and also working. I believe I can do something similar. It doesn't have to be either/or; it can be both/and! I just never saw my choices that way before."

Like Rachel, Jennifer knows her enthusiasm for these new possibilities will mean having to make more choices when she returns home. John had reluctantly agreed to her attending the convention when he realized she could still be in San Francisco in time for his awards dinner. Will he be enthusiastic about or frustrated with her new ideas? Will he see her new plans as fulfilling a part of who she is, or will he argue that her only real fulfillment should come from caring for her children (and him)? Jennifer knows she has her work cut out for her when she returns home, but she remains enthusiastic about the new choices she is discovering for herself.

MARIA'S STORY

"The convention so far has left me feeling reflective. This may sound strange to the rest of you, but for the first time I'm starting to see myself as a leader. This happened when I realized that my own desires need to play more prominently in the choices I make. I've done a pretty good job of leading my life up to this point, but I've never described myself as anything other than a single mother. The breakout sessions are helping me embrace the notion that I am also a leader. I feel like I have lots of possibilities ahead of me that I have never allowed myself to consider. When the keynote speaker talked about the distinction between self and selfish, I realized that I have always automatically done what I thought was best for my daughter, without considering my own wishes, and that dismissing my own needs was a selfish act! I thought that being a single mother meant a life of unending sacrifices . . . that it meant putting Patricia first, second, and third. I'm now expanding that paradigm to put some of my own desires in those top three spots. And here's the funny part: Patricia will be the first to agree!

"This new perspective of myself has me considering some different choices when I return home. I'm considering returning to college to get the certification that will allow me to apply for a job as principal in our school system. And now that I'm starting to see myself as a leader with my own dreams and wishes, why not?"

GRACE'S STORY

"I came here with lots of questions, seeking lots of answers. What I'm beginning to understand is that there is no one right answer for any of my questions. I guess I thought that there would be a right choice and a wrong choice, or a good choice and a bad choice, and the convention would help me sort those out. The keynote speaker reminded me that ,for the most part, our choices are rarely between good and evil, as we ministers might say. Rather, our choices are more often than not between that which is good and that which is better. Or between that which is better and that which is best.

"From a 'calling' perspective, I'm beginning to conclude that God trusts me to determine which choice is best for me. I guess there's no escaping that any way you look at it, our choices are up to us. It helps to be clear about what we want so we can have a good idea of what the best choice is.

"I'm heading back to my church with the confidence that there is not a wrong choice to make. I've decided to share with my congregation the invitation I've received from the denomination and let them help me determine what the right choice is. After all, they're my family and I wouldn't want to leave them out of this decision. What I'm learning here is that either way I choose, I win. I think that's the message God sent me here to get."

KATHY'S STORY

"Whatever confusion I came here with has been heightened with what I'm learning! Concerning my decision whether to run for mayor, I really do want what's best for everyone. I'm realizing, though, that trying to please all of the people all of the time is a hopeless and frustrating ambition. I have to choose what's best for me in the context of all of the roles I enjoy: public servant, mother, spouse, grandmother, and community activist. Up until now, those roles have felt balanced. Choosing to run for mayor would mean redefining that balance.

"When I share my 'story' with other women at the convention, they tell me they think I would be a great mayoral candidate and a role model for women in politics.   They seem to have a lot of confidence in my ability to pull it off. I've almost convinced myself that I can succeed as well.   The question that remains is, do I really want to?

"I came here with two questions and now I have ten! The good news is that I see more clearly the choices before me.   Now I have to decide what's best for me, and then get everyone around me to support that decision!   Whoever said, 'If it's to be it's up to me" must have had my situation in mind.   It's a good thing we never run out of choices."

!
EPILOGUE

I *t's Saturday afternoon and the convention is winding down. Jennifer has already left for San Francisco to see her husband receive his sales award, but not before promising to join Rachel, Maria, Grace, and Kathy at next year's Intention Convention. They plan to share their stories about the new directions their choices will have taken them. Promising to stay in touch by phone and e-mail, they exchange their heartfelt good-byes.*

Each of the women has a final reflection on what this adventure has been about.

RACHEL

Rachel goes back home with more confidence about her future. She's already planning to ask the company to provide tuition reimbursement so she can finish college and get her marketing degree. She has already called her boss and asked for time on his calendar to share her ideas about her own future and that of the

company. She's also told her family that she has some
important things to share with them. She knows their
input and support are crucial to her plans.

*At the Intention Convention next year, will Rachel have
finished two semesters of college? Will her company be
paying for that education? Will her role at Glendale
Manufacturing have been redefined? And what about
her family role? Will that have been redefined as well?
What has Rachel learned about herself as a woman?*

JENNIFER

Jennifer has left the convention early to attend her
husband's National Sales ceremony. She is flush with
excitement as she thinks about launching a home-
based business. She has to redefine her partnership
with her husband so that she can successfully balance
her mother/wife role with her role as a businesswoman.
Jennifer also knows she wants to talk more with
her friend Lynn who has concluded that she has no
choices of her own.

*Will Jennifer succeed in starting her home-based business?
Will she and her husband John succeed in redefining
their marital partnership and the responsibilities that each
brings to the family? What conversation will Jennifer have
with her friend Lynn that will begin to open Lynn's eyes
to the real choices in her life? What will Jennifer have
learned about herself as a woman? Or, when all is said*

*and done, will Jennifer conclude that being a stay-at-home
mom really is all the fulfillment she seeks?*

MARIA

Through her participation in the convention, her
appreciation of self has been significantly heightened.
She is now considering submitting her application for
the certification program that would eventually enable
her to apply for a position as a high school principal.
She is excited about going home and talking with
Patricia about the possibilities she now sees for herself.
She realizes that Patricia's role has been as a great
teacher as well as a great daughter.

*Will Maria choose to enroll in the certification program
that would enable her to be a principal? And how will
her new sense of self impact the relationship she has with
herself and with her daughter? Will she stay in the Air
Force Reserves? There is a rumor that they may be called
to active duty in the next ninety days. How would that
affect her possibilities of her returning to school? And
what has Maria learned about herself as a woman?*

GRACE

Grace returns home knowing that whatever choice
she makes, it's the right one. After all, there is no
wrong choice and there is always a next choice. She
finds herself yearning to be surrounded again by the

congregation she has come to know as her family. She is eager to share her experience, learning, and insights from this convention. Grace wants her congregation to share in the decision she faces about whether to accept the new role the denomination has offered her.

Does Grace choose to stay with her congregation family or will she accept the invitation to take on a leadership role in the denomination? How will her congregation respond? How will the denomination leadership respond? Will there be other callings in Grace's life? What has Grace learned about herself as a woman?

KATHY

Kathy leaves the convention with the recognition that her decision goes far beyond herself, and even her family. She has come to realize that running for mayor would position her as a role model for other women who might be consider campaigning for office. Throwing her hat in the ring would be more significant than she had thought before attending the convention. Kathy has decided to file her application to run for mayor, recognizing that she and her husband will have to reevaluate their plans for retirement.

Will Kathy win her election? What will the campaign have been like as the first time a woman ran for mayor in Quincy? What will have happened to the family roles that have been so important to Kathy, and so comfortable? What will she have learned about herself in running for mayor? What will she have learned about herself as a woman?

And the last big question is:

Where will you, the reader, find the answers to the questions these five women now face? It's as easy as eventually "turning the page" when the second in this series of books about women and their choices is published.

When we wrote this book, we always had three books in mind. This book focuses on women being clear about what they want, asking for it, and holding their boundaries—for themselves. Our second book (coming soon) entitled, *Choose Again,* reveals answers to the questions Rachel, Jennifer, Maria, Grace, and Kathy are seeking with some surprises along the way. We'll introduce you to new characters and tell a story about women choosing to support other women and how such choices enrich and provide opportunities for all of us.

Our third book, *Now Choose One More Time,* takes a longer-term view of the choices we're making today. What impact it has on our lives, the lives of our daughters and even our granddaughters. Beginning with the end in mind, please join us as we explore and choose the legacy we'll leave to generations of women to come.

About the Auth!rs

DOTTIE GANDY

Dottie is an author, speaker, and facilitator who has spent more than thirty-five years as a business executive and successful entrepreneur. She is the author of *Thirty Days to a Happy Employee* and is a co-founder of the National Association of Women Business Owners. A former regional director for the Franklin Covey Company, Ms. Gandy now resides in Allen, Texas, with her husband Tom. She has two daughters, one stepson, and four extraordinary grandchildren. Dottie is a graduate of Baylor University.

MARSHA CLARK

Marsha Clark is a businesswoman, author, coach, and consultant, whose passion is helping women to explore, discover, and fulfill their purpose and potential in life. She has more than thirty years of business experience in the technology industry and now owns her own business, Marsha Clark & Associates. With the help of a generous and competent advisory team, she developed a year-long women's leadership development program, The POWER of Self. Marsha now reside in Frisco, Texas, with her husband Dale. She is a graduate of American University.

A Note to Our Readers

Although an actual intention convention has not been scheduled, a number of our women friends and colleagues have suggested that we consider hosting one. If you have an interest in such a meeting, or have additional suggestions or ideas, we welcome your comments.

Dottie Gandy
www.dottiegandy.com

Marsha Clark
www.powerofself.com